।। श्री हनुमा

CENTRAL CHINMAYA MISSION TRUST

MUMBAI - 400 072.

Total no. of copies printed till - 2007 - 2009 - 8,000 copies
Reprinted March - 2011 - 2,000 copies

Published by :
CENTRAL CHINMAYA MISSION TRUST
Sandeepany Sadhanalaya
Saki Vihar Road,
Mumbai-400 072, INDIA.
Tel. : (91-22)2857 2367/ 5806 / 2828
Fax :(91-22) 2857 3065
Email : ccmtpublications@chinmayamission.com
Website :www.chinmayamission.com

Distribution Centre in USA :
CHINMAYA MISSION WEST
Publications Division,
560 Bridgetown Pike, Langhorne, PA 19053, USA
Tel. : (215) 396-0390
Fax : (215) 396-9710
Email : publications@chinmayamission.org
Website : www.chinmayapublications.org

Illustrations :
Bharati Sukhatankar

Printed by :
JAK Printers Pvt Ltd.

Price : Rs. 150.00

ISBN : 9788175974029

Pujya Gurudev Swami Chinmayananda

WHY HANUMAN CHALISA

Like most children, Hanuman too, was a naughty child. Once, in great mischief, he created havoc in a Rishi's ashram. The Rishi pronounced that Hanuman would not remember his great strength, prowess and extraordinary abilities till he was reminded about them.

When we chant Hanuman Chalisa, we remind Hanumanji about these and invoke his blessings upon us.

That is the reason why Hanumanji never fails us.

Jai Hanuman ! Jai Sri Ram !

2nd April, 2007
HANUMAN JAYANTI **Central Chinmaya Mission Trust**

दोहा

श्रीगुरू चरन सरोज रज

निज मनु मुकुरू सुधारि ।

बरनऊँ रघुबर बिमल जसु

जो दायकु फल चारि ।।

DOHA

Sri Guru charan saroj raj,

nij man mukuru sudhari,

Baranau Raghubar bimalajasu,

jo dayaku phal chari.

With the dust from the Guru's lotus feet, I first clean the mirror of my heart and then narrate the sacred glory of Sri Ram (Raghubar), supreme in the Raghu dynasty, giver of the fourfold goals of life[1].

1. The fourfold goals are Kama, Artha, Dharma and Moksha i.e. pleasure, wealth, religious-merit and salvation.

बुद्धिहीन तनु जानिके

सुमिरौं पवन कुमार ।

बल बुधि बिद्या देहु मोहिं

हरहु कलेस बिकार ।।

Buddhi heen tanu janike

Sumirow Pavan Kumar,

Bal budhi bidya dehu mohi

Harahu kales bikar.

Knowing myself to be ignorant, I request you, O Hanuman, son of Pavan[1]! Bestow upon me strength, wisdom and knowledge, taking away all my miseries and blemishes.

1. Wind God

चौपाई

जय हनुमान ज्ञान गुन सागर ।

जय कपीस तिहुँ लोक उजागर ।।

CHOWPAI

Jai Hanuman gyan guna sagar,

Jai Kapees tihun lok ujagar.

Victory to Thee, O Hanuman, ocean of wisdom and virtue! Victory to the Lord of monkeys who is well known in all the three worlds.

राम दूत अतुलित बल धामा ।
अंजनि पुत्र पवनसुत नामा ।।

Ramdoot atulit bal dhama,
Anjani-putra Pavanasuta nama.

You are the messenger of Ram and the storehouse of immeasurable strength; you are known as Anjaniputra and Pavanasuta[1].

1. Son of Anjani, Son of Pavan

महाबीर बिक्रम बजरंगी ।
कुमति निवार सुमति के संगी ।।

Mahabeer Bikram Bajrangi,
Kumati nivaar sumati ke sangi.

O Mahaveer (mighty brave), you are strong and powerful, your body tough as Vajra[1]. Ever in the company of the good and wise you dispel evil thoughts (from the mind).

1. Weapon of Indra

कंचन बरन बिराज सुबेसा ।
कानन कुंडल कुंचित केसा ।।

Kanchan baran biraj subesa,
Kanan kundal kunchit kesa.

Your body has a golden glow. You are beautifully dressed wearing earrings, and you have curly hair.

जय श्री राम

हाथ बज्र औ ध्वजा बिराजे ।
कांधे मूंज जनेऊ साजे ।।

Haath bajra au dhvaja biraje,
Kandhe moonj janeu saje.

You hold the mace of vajra and a flag in your hands, and have the sacred thread of Munja grass adorning your shoulder.

शंकर सुवन केसरीनंदन ।
तेज प्रताप महा जग बंदन ।।

Shankar suvan Kesari nandan,
Tej pratap maha jag bandan.

Reincarnation of Lord Shankar[1] and the son of Kesari[2], your great lustre and glory are praised by the whole world.

1. Hanuman is considered as the 11th Rudra avatar.
2. Kesari is the monkey king, husband of Anjani.

विद्यावान गुनी अति चातुर ।
राम काज करिबे को आतुर ।।

Vidyavan guni ati chatur,
Ram kaj karibe ko atur.

Full of knowledge, wisdom and virtue, you are always eager to serve Lord Ram.

प्रभु चरित्र सुनिबे को रसिया ।
राम लखन सीता मन बसिया ।।

Prabhu charitra sunibe ko rasiya,
Ram Lakhan Sita man basiya.

You are ever eager to listen to the glories of the Lord, and Ram, Lakshman and Sita always dwell in your heart.

सूक्ष्म रूप धरि सियहिं दिखावा ।
बिकट रूप धरि लंक जरावा ।।

Sookshma roop dhari Siyahin dikhawa,
Bikata roop dhari lanka jarawa.

You appeared before Sita in small (and acceptable) form, while you assumed a huge and awesome form when you burnt Lanka.

भीम रूप धरि असुर सँहारे ।
रामचंद्र के काज सँवारे ।।

Bheem roop dhari asur sanhare,
Ramchandra ke kaj sanvare.

You assumed a huge, gigantic form and killed the demons, thus fulfilling the mission of Sri Ram.

लाय सजीवन लखन जियाये ।
श्रीरघुबीर हरषि उर लाये ।।

Laye sajeevan Lakhan jiyaye,
Sri Raghubeer harashi ur laye.

You brought the Sanjivani[1] herb and revived Lakshman; with great joy, Sri Ram embraced you.

1. Life restoring herb.

रघुपति कीन्ही बहुत बडाई ।
तुम मम प्रिय भरतहि सम भाई ।।

Raghupati keenhi bahut badai,
Tum mama priya Bharat hi sam bhai.

Sri Ram (Raghupati) praised you highly and said that you were as dear to him as his brother Bharat.

सहस बदन तुम्हरो जस गावैं ।
अस कहि श्रीपति कंठ लगावै ।।

Sahasa badana tumhro jas gavein,
Asa kahi Sripati kanth lagavein.

" Your glory is sung by Sheshanaag[1]," said Sri Ram, (Sri-pati = Lord of Lakshmi), and embraced you.

1. Thousand - headed serpent, on whom Lord Vishnu rests.

सनकादिक ब्रह्मादि मुनीसा ।
नारद सारद सहित अहीसा ।।

Sanakadik Brahmadi muneesa,
Narad Sarad sahit ahisaa.

Sanaka[1] and others, Brahma[2], other gods, Narada, Sharada (Saraswati) and Shesha.....

1. The sages Sanaka, Sanatana, Sanandana and Sanat Kumar
2. The Creator.

जम कुबेर दिगपाल जहाँ ते ।
कबि कोबिद कहिं सके कहाँ ते ।।

Jam Kuber Digpal jahan te,
Kabi kobid kahin sake kahan te.

Yama[1], Kuber [2], Digpalas [3], poets and seers, have all failed to describe your glory.

1. God of Death
2. God of Wealth
3. Gods of the Directions.

तुम उपकार सुग्रीवहिं कीन्हा ।
राम मिलाय राज पद दीन्हा ।।

Tum upkar Sugreevahin keenha,
Ram milay rajpad deenha.

You helped Sugreeva[1] greatly – you introduced him to Sri Ram and helped him get back his throne.

1. Sugreeva was a monkey king.

तुम्हरो मंत्र बिभीषन माना ।
लंकेश्वर भए सब जग जाना ।।

Tumharo mantra Bibheeshan mana,
Lankeshwar bhaye sab jag jana.

Vibheeshan[1] listened to your advice and the whole world knows, he became King of Lanka.

1. Younger brother of Ravana, was crowned King of Lanka after Ravana's death.

जुग सहस्त्र जोजन पर भानू ।
लील्यो ताहि मधुर फल जानू ।।

Jug sahasra jojan par bhanu,
Leelyo tahi madhur phal janu.

You swallowed the sun, millions of miles away, taking it to be a sweet fruit.

प्रभु मुद्रिका मेलि मुख माहीं ।
जलधि लाँघि गये अचरज नाहीं ।।

Prabhu mudrika meli mukha maheen,
Jaladhi langhi gaye acharaj naheen.

Keeping the Lord's ring in your mouth, you crossed the mighty ocean[1].

1. In search of Sita.

दुर्गम काज जगत के जेते ।
सुगम अनुग्रह तुम्हरे तेते ।।

Durgam kaj jagat ke jete,
Sugam anugrah tumhre te te.

With your grace, all the obstacles and difficulties of the world can be easily overcome.

राम दुआरे तुम रखवारे ।
होत न आज्ञा बिनु पैसारे ।।

Ram duare tum rakhavare,
Hoat na aagya binu paisare.

You are the sentinel of Sri Ram's abode, where no one can enter without your permission.

सब सुख लहै तुम्हारी सरना ।
तुम रक्षक काहू को डर ना ।।

Sab sukh lahai tumhari sarna,
Tum rakshak kahu ko darna.

He who takes refuge in you enjoys all happiness. Why should anyone have fear when you are the protector?

आपन तेज सम्हारो आपै ।
तीनों लोक हाँक तें काँपै ।।

Aapan tej samharo apai,
Tino lok hank te kanpai.

You alone can control your own might and power; all three worlds tremble when you roar.

भूत पिशाच निकट नहिं आवै ।
महाबीर जब नाम सुनावै ।।

Bhoot pishach nikat nahi avai,
Mahabeer jab naam sunavai.

Evil spirits and ghosts dare not come anywhere near him who chants your name, Mahaveer.

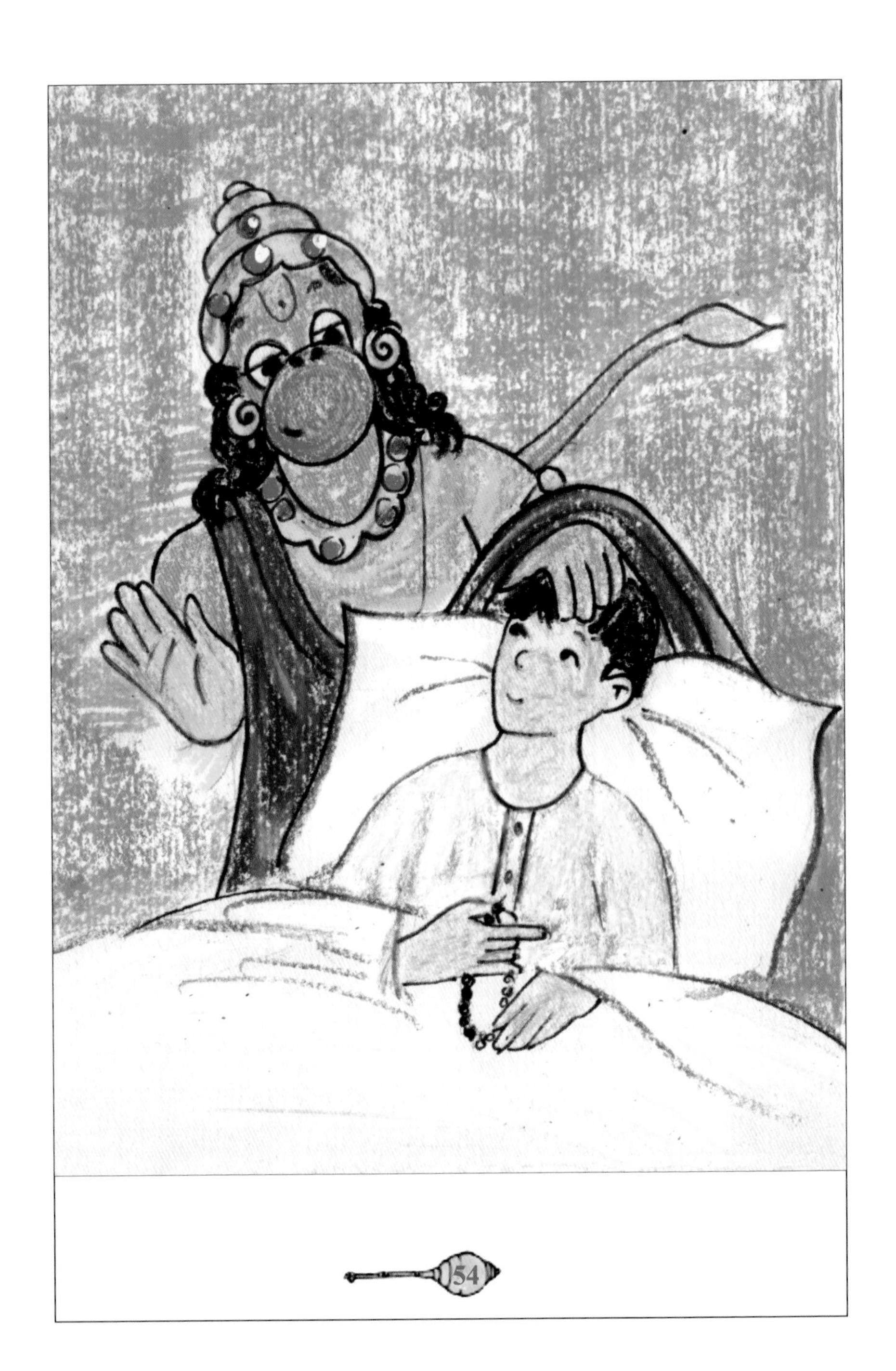

नासै रोग हरै सब पीरा ।
जपत निरंतर हनुमत बीरा ।।

Nasai rog hare sab peera,
Japat nirantar Hanumat beera.

O Hanuman, all diseases are cured and all pains disappear when one chants your name constantly.

संकट तें हनुमान छुडावै ।
मन क्रम बचन ध्यान जो लावै ।।

Sankat te Hanuman chhudavai,
Man kram bachan dhyan jo lavai.

Hanuman frees from all troubles, him who contemplates on him in thought, word and deed.

राम
राम
राम
राम
राम
राम
श्री राम
श्री राम
श्री राम
श्री राम

सब पर राम तपस्वी राजा ।
तिन के काज सकल तुम साजा ।।

Sab par Ram tapasvi raja,
Tinke kaj sakal tum saja.

Sri Ram, the ascetic King, is the ruler of all, and you fulfilled all his missions.

और मनोरथ जो कोई लावै ।
सोई अमित जीवन फल पावै ।।

Aur manorath jo koi lavai,
Soi amit jeevan phal pavai.

Anyone coming to you with any desire, achieves the goal of life's fulfilment.

चारों जुग परताप तुम्हारा ।
है परसिद्ध जगत उजियारा ।।

Charo jug partap tumhara,
Hai parsiddha jagat ujiyara.

Your glory spreads over the four Yugas[1] and your fame radiates all over the world.

1. Satya, Dwapar, Treta and Kali.

साधु संत के तुम रखवारे ।
असुर निकंदन राम दुलारे ।।

Sadhu sant ke tum rakhavare,
Asur nikandan Ram dulare.

You are the protector of saints and sages, the destroyer of demons and beloved of Sri Ram.

अष्ट सिद्धि नौ निधि के दाता ।
अस बर दीन जानकी माता ।।

Ashta siddhi nou nidhi ke data,
As bar deen Janaki mata.

Mother Janaki[1] has blessed you with the power to bestow (upon anyone) the eight powers[2] and nine wealths[3].

1. Sita
2. Ashta Siddhi - ***anima*** - reducing one's size to that of an atom; ***mahima*** - expanding one's size; ***garima*** - becoming very heavy; ***laghima*** - becoming very light; ***prapti*** - unrestricted access to places; ***prakamya*** -getting whatever you desire; ***ishitva*** - lordship; ***vashitva*** - subjugating others
3. Nau nidhi-nine types of wealth.

राम रसायन तुम्हरे पासा ।
सदा रहो रघुपति के दासा ।।

Ram rasayan tumhare pasa,
Sada raho Raghupati ke dasa.

May you always remain in the service of Sri Ram (Raghupati), the essence of whose devotion is with you.

तुम्हरे भजन राम को पावै।
जनम जनम के दुख बिसरावै ।।

Tumhre bhajan Ram ko pavai,
Janam janam ke dukh bisravai.

Devotion to you brings one to Ram, and the sorrows of many lives are wiped away.

अंत काल रघुबर पुर जाई ।
जहाँ जन्म हरि भक्त कहाई ।।

Anta kal Raghubar pur jai,
Jahan janma Hari Bhakta kahai.

At the end of a life of such devotion, he goes to the abode of Sri Ram, where he comes to be known as a devotee of the Lord (Hari-bhakta).

और देवता चित्त न धरई ।
हनुमत सेई सर्व सुख करई ।।

Aur devata chitta na dharai,
Hanumat sei sarva sukh karai.

He who serves you, Hanuman, gets all happiness; there is no need to worship any other deity.

संकट कटै मिटै सब पीरा ।
जो सुमिरै हनुमत बलबीरा ।।

Sankat katai mitai sab peera,
Jo sumirai Hanumat balbeera.

All the difficulties and pains are removed, of those who invoke the all-powerful Hanuman.

जै जै जै हनुमान गोसाईं ।
कृपा करहु गुरु देव की नाईं ।।

Jai Jai Jai Hanuman gosain,
Kripa karahu Gurudev ki nain.

Victory to you, O Hanuman, three times over. As our divine teacher, be compassionate towards us.

जो शत बार पाठ कर कोई ।
छूटहि बंदि महा सुख होई ।।

Jo shat bar path kar koi,
Chhootahi bandi maha sukh hoi.

He who chants this one hundred times, gets liberated from earthly bondage and attains supreme bliss.

जो यह पढ़ै हनुमान चालीसा ।
होय सिद्धि साखी गौरीसा ।।

Jo yah padhai Hanuman Chalisa,
Hoy siddhi sakhi Gourisa.

He who reads these forty verses of Hanuman (Hanuman Chalisa), attains perfection. Lord Shiva is witness to this.

तुलसीदास सदा हरि चेरा ।
कीजै नाथ हृदय मँह डेरा ।।

Tulsidas sada Hari chera,
Keejai nath hriday mah dera.

Tulsidas[1], ever the servant of Sri Ram (Hari Chera), prays, "Lord, please, always reside in my heart".

1. The author of these verses.

दोहा

पवनतनय संकट हरन,

मंगल मूरति रूप ।

राम लखन सीता सहित

हृदय बसहु सुर भूप ।।

DOHA

Pavan tanay sankat haran

Mangal moorti roop,

Ram Lakhan Sita sahit

Hriday basahu sur bhoop.

May Hanuman (Pavan Tanay), the remover of difficulties, of auspicious form, ever reside in my heart, along with Ram, Lakshman and Sita.

आरती

मंगल मूरति मारुत नंदन ।

सकल अमंगल मूल निकंदन ।।१।।

पवनतनय संतन हितकारी ।

हृदय बिराजत अवध बिहारी ।।२।।

मातु पिता गुरु गनपति सारद ।

सिवा समेत संभु सुक नारद ।।३।।

चरन बंदि बिनवौं सब काहू ।

देहु रामपद नेह निबाहू ।।४।।

बंदौं राम लखन बैदेही ।

ये तुलसी के परम सनेही ।।५।।

ARATI

Mangal Moorti Marut nandan

Sakal amangal mool nikandan

Pawanatanaya santan hitakari

Hridaya biraajat Awadh Bihari

Maatu Pita Guru Ganapati Saarad

Sivaa samet Sambhu Suk Naarad

Charan bandi binvaun sab kaahu

Dehu Rampad neh nibahu

Bandau Ram Lakhan Baidehi

Yeh Tulsi ke param Sanehi.

OTHER TITLES IN THE BALVIHAR SERIES

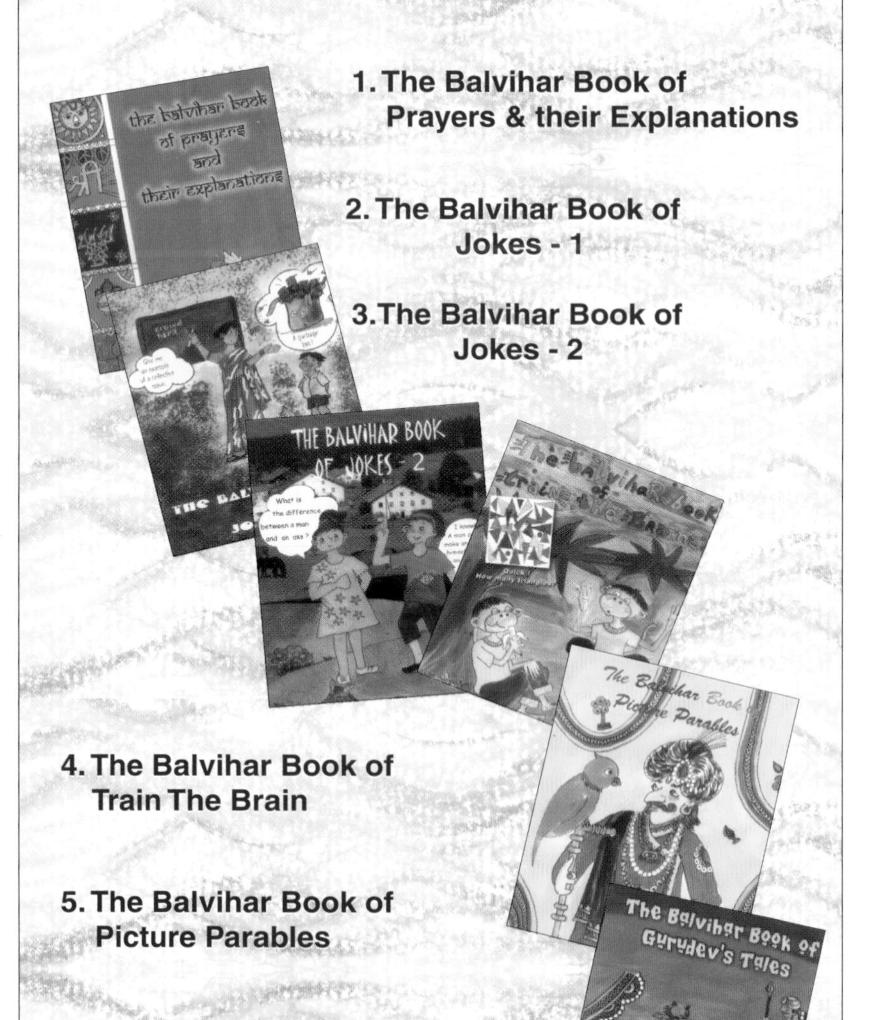

1. The Balvihar Book of Prayers & their Explanations
2. The Balvihar Book of Jokes - 1
3. The Balvihar Book of Jokes - 2
4. The Balvihar Book of Train The Brain
5. The Balvihar Book of Picture Parables
6. The Balvihar Book of Gurudev's Tales

FORTHCOMING TITLES IN THIS SERIES

1. The Balvihar Book of Saintly Wisdom
2. The Balvihar Book of Activity
3. The Balvihar Book of One - Act Plays
4. The Balvihar Book of Inner Beauty
5. The Balvihar Book of Mom and Dad
6. The Balvihar Book of This and That